worship & praise

Let Us PRAY

prayer journal for kids

This journal belongs to:

_____

FOR A LITTLE INSPIRATION
follow along at:

⟳ @JUNEANDLUCY

📘 @JUNEANDLUCY

WWW.JUNELUCY.COM

✉ **Hey, parents!** Join our newsletter by emailing us at **freebies@junelucy.com** to receive freebies, discounts and sales info. Let us know which book you bought by putting the book title in the subject line of your email.

Shop our other books at
www.junelucy.com

For questions and customer service, email us at
support@junelucy.com

TODAY'S DATE: _____ S M T W Th F S

× × × × × × × × × × ×

DEAR GOD

TODAY I THANK YOU FOR:

1. _____

2. _____

3. _____

TODAY I ASK YOU FOR: _____

_____

TODAY I AM PRAYING FOR THESE PEOPLE:

1. _____

2. _____

3. _____

TODAY'S BIBLE VERSE/STORY: _____

_____

_____

now I lay me down to sleep....

TONIGHT I PRAY FOR: _____

TONIGHT I THANK GOD FOR: _____

TONIGHT _____
    IS ON MY HEART

amen.

TODAY'S DATE: _____ S M T W Th F S

✗ ✗ ✗ ✗ ✗ ✗ ✗ ✗ ✗ ✗ ✗

DEAR GOD

TODAY I THANK YOU FOR:

1. _____
2. _____
3. _____

TODAY I ASK YOU FOR: _____
_____

TODAY I AM PRAYING FOR THESE PEOPLE:

1. _____
2. _____
3. _____

TODAY'S BIBLE VERSE/STORY: _____
_____
_____

now I lay me down to sleep....

TONIGHT I PRAY FOR: _____

TONIGHT I THANK GOD FOR: _____

TONIGHT _____
IS ON MY HEART

amen.

TODAY'S DATE: _____ S M T W Th F S

✗ ✗ ✗ ✗ ✗ ✗ ✗ ✗ ✗ ✗ ✗

DEAR GOD

TODAY I THANK YOU FOR:

1. _____

2. _____

3. _____

TODAY I ASK YOU FOR: _____

_____

TODAY I AM PRAYING FOR THESE PEOPLE:

1. _____

2. _____

3. _____

TODAY'S BIBLE VERSE/STORY: _____

_____

_____

now I lay me down to sleep....

TONIGHT I PRAY FOR: _____

TONIGHT I THANK GOD FOR: _____

TONIGHT _____
    IS ON MY HEART

amen.

TODAY'S DATE: _____ S M T W Th F S

✗ ✗ ✗ ✗ ✗ ✗ ✗ ✗ ✗ ✗ ✗ ✗

DEAR GOD

TODAY I THANK YOU FOR:

1. _____
2. _____
3. _____

TODAY I ASK YOU FOR: _____

_____

TODAY I AM PRAYING FOR THESE PEOPLE:

1. _____
2. _____
3. _____

TODAY'S BIBLE VERSE/STORY: _____

_____

_____

now I lay me down to sleep....

TONIGHT I PRAY FOR: _____

TONIGHT I THANK GOD FOR: _____

TONIGHT _____
    IS ON MY HEART

amen.

TODAY'S DATE: _____ S M T W Th F S

× × × × × × × × × × ×

DEAR GOD

TODAY I THANK YOU FOR:

1. _____

2. _____

3. _____

TODAY I ASK YOU FOR: _____

_____

TODAY I AM PRAYING FOR THESE PEOPLE:

1. _____

2. _____

3. _____

TODAY'S BIBLE VERSE/STORY: _____

_____

_____

now I lay me down to sleep....

TONIGHT I PRAY FOR: _____

TONIGHT I THANK GOD FOR: _____

TONIGHT _____
IS ON MY HEART

amen.

TODAY'S DATE: _____ S M T W Th F S

✗ ✗ ✗ ✗ ✗ ✗ ✗ ✗ ✗ ✗ ✗ ✗

DEAR GOD

TODAY I THANK YOU FOR:

1. _____

2. _____

3. _____

TODAY I ASK YOU FOR: _____

_____

TODAY I AM PRAYING FOR THESE PEOPLE:

1. _____

2. _____

3. _____

TODAY'S BIBLE VERSE/STORY: _____

_____

_____

now I lay me down to sleep....

TONIGHT I PRAY FOR: _____

TONIGHT I THANK GOD FOR: _____

TONIGHT _____
   IS ON MY HEART

amen.

TODAY'S DATE: _____ S M T W Th F S

✗ ✗ ✗ ✗ ✗ ✗ ✗ ✗ ✗ ✗ ✗

DEAR GOD

TODAY I THANK YOU FOR:

1. _____

2. _____

3. _____

TODAY I ASK YOU FOR: _____

_____

TODAY I AM PRAYING FOR THESE PEOPLE:

1. _____

2. _____

3. _____

TODAY'S BIBLE VERSE/STORY: _____

_____

_____

now I lay me down to sleep....

TONIGHT I PRAY FOR: _____

TONIGHT I THANK GOD FOR: _____

TONIGHT _____
   IS ON MY HEART

amen.

TODAY'S DATE: _____   S M T W Th F S

✕ ✕ ✕ ✕ ✕ ✕ ✕ ✕ ✕ ✕ ✕

DEAR GOD

TODAY I THANK YOU FOR:

1. _____

2. _____

3. _____

TODAY I ASK YOU FOR: _____

_____

TODAY I AM PRAYING FOR THESE PEOPLE:

1. _____

2. _____

3. _____

TODAY'S BIBLE VERSE/STORY: _____

_____

_____

now I lay me down to sleep....

TONIGHT I PRAY FOR: _____

TONIGHT I THANK GOD FOR: _____

TONIGHT _____
    IS ON MY HEART

amen.

TODAY'S DATE: _____   S M T W Th F S

✕ ✕ ✕ ✕ ✕ ✕ ✕ ✕ ✕ ✕ ✕

DEAR GOD

TODAY I THANK YOU FOR:

1. _____

2. _____

3. _____

TODAY I ASK YOU FOR: _____

_____

TODAY I AM PRAYING FOR THESE PEOPLE:

1. _____

2. _____

3. _____

TODAY'S BIBLE VERSE/STORY: _____

_____

_____

now I lay me down to sleep....

TONIGHT I PRAY FOR: _____

TONIGHT I THANK GOD FOR: _____

TONIGHT _____
    IS ON MY HEART

amen.

TODAY'S DATE: _____ S M T W Th F S

✗ ✗ ✗ ✗ ✗ ✗ ✗ ✗ ✗ ✗ ✗ ✗

TODAY I THANK YOU FOR:

DEAR GOD

   1. _____

   2. _____

   3. _____

TODAY I ASK YOU FOR: _____

_____

TODAY I AM PRAYING FOR THESE PEOPLE:

   1. _____

   2. _____

   3. _____

TODAY'S BIBLE VERSE/STORY: _____

_____

_____

now I lay me down to sleep....

TONIGHT I PRAY FOR: _____

TONIGHT I THANK GOD FOR: _____

TONIGHT _____
  IS ON MY HEART

amen.

I AM FEARFULLY AND WONDERFULLY MADE.

Psalm 139:14

TODAY'S DATE: _____ S M T W Th F S

✕ ✕ ✕ ✕ ✕ ✕ ✕ ✕ ✕ ✕ ✕

DEAR GOD

TODAY I THANK YOU FOR:

1. _____
2. _____
3. _____

TODAY I ASK YOU FOR: _____

_____

TODAY I AM PRAYING FOR THESE PEOPLE:

1. _____
2. _____
3. _____

TODAY'S BIBLE VERSE/STORY: _____

_____

_____

now I lay me down to sleep....

TONIGHT I PRAY FOR: _____

TONIGHT I THANK GOD FOR: _____

TONIGHT _____
    IS ON MY HEART

amen.

TODAY'S DATE: _____ S M T W Th F S

× × × × × × × × × × ×

DEAR GOD

TODAY I THANK YOU FOR:

1. _____

2. _____

3. _____

TODAY I ASK YOU FOR: _____

_____

TODAY I AM PRAYING FOR THESE PEOPLE:

1. _____

2. _____

3. _____

TODAY'S BIBLE VERSE/STORY: _____

_____

_____

now I lay me down to sleep....

TONIGHT I PRAY FOR: _____

TONIGHT I THANK GOD FOR: _____

TONIGHT _____
    IS ON MY HEART

amen.

TODAY'S DATE: _____ S M T W Th F S

✗ ✗ ✗ ✗ ✗ ✗ ✗ ✗ ✗ ✗ ✗

DEAR GOD

TODAY I THANK YOU FOR:

1. _____

2. _____

3. _____

TODAY I ASK YOU FOR: _____

_____

TODAY I AM PRAYING FOR THESE PEOPLE:

1. _____

2. _____

3. _____

TODAY'S BIBLE VERSE/STORY: _____

_____

_____

now I lay me down to sleep....

TONIGHT I PRAY FOR: _____

TONIGHT I THANK GOD FOR: _____

TONIGHT _____
    IS ON MY HEART

amen.

TODAY'S DATE: _____ S M T W Th F S

✕ ✕ ✕ ✕ ✕ ✕ ✕ ✕ ✕ ✕ ✕ **DEAR GOD**

TODAY I THANK YOU FOR:

1. _____

2. _____

3. _____

TODAY I ASK YOU FOR: _____

_____

TODAY I AM PRAYING FOR THESE PEOPLE:

1. _____

2. _____

3. _____

TODAY'S BIBLE VERSE/STORY: _____

_____

_____

now I lay me down to sleep....

TONIGHT I PRAY FOR: _____

TONIGHT I THANK GOD FOR: _____

TONIGHT _____
    IS ON MY HEART

amen.

TODAY'S DATE: _____ S M T W Th F S

✕ ✕ ✕ ✕ ✕ ✕ ✕ ✕ ✕ ✕ ✕ **DEAR GOD**

TODAY I THANK YOU FOR:

1. _____

2. _____

3. _____

TODAY I ASK YOU FOR: _____

_____

TODAY I AM PRAYING FOR THESE PEOPLE:

1. _____

2. _____

3. _____

TODAY'S BIBLE VERSE/STORY: _____

_____

_____

now I lay me down to sleep....

TONIGHT I PRAY FOR: _____

TONIGHT I THANK GOD FOR: _____

TONIGHT _____
    IS ON MY HEART

amen.

TODAY'S DATE: _____ S M T W Th F S

✕ ✕ ✕ ✕ ✕ ✕ ✕ ✕ ✕ ✕ ✕

DEAR GOD

TODAY I THANK YOU FOR:

1. _____

2. _____

3. _____

TODAY I ASK YOU FOR: _____

_____

TODAY I AM PRAYING FOR THESE PEOPLE:

1. _____

2. _____

3. _____

TODAY'S BIBLE VERSE/STORY: _____

_____

_____

now I lay me down to sleep....

TONIGHT I PRAY FOR: _____

TONIGHT I THANK GOD FOR: _____

TONIGHT _____
    IS ON MY HEART

amen.

TODAY'S DATE: _____ S M T W Th F S

× × × × × × × × × × ×

TODAY I THANK YOU FOR:

DEAR GOD

   1. _____

   2. _____

   3. _____

TODAY I ASK YOU FOR: _____

_____

TODAY I AM PRAYING FOR THESE PEOPLE:

   1. _____

   2. _____

   3. _____

TODAY'S BIBLE VERSE/STORY: _____

_____

_____

now I lay me down to sleep....

TONIGHT I PRAY FOR: _____

TONIGHT I THANK GOD FOR: _____

TONIGHT _____
   IS ON MY HEART

amen.

TODAY'S DATE: _____ S M T W Th F S

x x x x x x x x x x x

DEAR GOD

TODAY I THANK YOU FOR:

1. _____
2. _____
3. _____

TODAY I ASK YOU FOR: _____

_____

TODAY I AM PRAYING FOR THESE PEOPLE:

1. _____
2. _____
3. _____

TODAY'S BIBLE VERSE/STORY: _____

_____

_____

now I lay me down to sleep....

TONIGHT I PRAY FOR: _____

TONIGHT I THANK GOD FOR: _____

TONIGHT _____
   IS ON MY HEART

amen.

THE LORD IS MY STRENGTH AND MY SHIELD.

Psalm 28:7

TODAY'S DATE: _____ S M T W Th F S

✗ ✗ ✗ ✗ ✗ ✗ ✗ ✗ ✗ ✗

DEAR GOD

TODAY I THANK YOU FOR:

1. _____

2. _____

3. _____

TODAY I ASK YOU FOR: _____

_____

TODAY I AM PRAYING FOR THESE PEOPLE:

1. _____

2. _____

3. _____

TODAY'S BIBLE VERSE/STORY: _____

_____

_____

now I lay me down to sleep....

TONIGHT I PRAY FOR: _____

TONIGHT I THANK GOD FOR: _____

TONIGHT _____
    IS ON MY HEART

amen.

TODAY'S DATE: _____ S M T W Th F S

✗ ✗ ✗ ✗ ✗ ✗ ✗ ✗ ✗ ✗ ✗

DEAR GOD

TODAY I THANK YOU FOR:

1. _____

2. _____

3. _____

TODAY I ASK YOU FOR: _____

_____

TODAY I AM PRAYING FOR THESE PEOPLE:

1. _____

2. _____

3. _____

TODAY'S BIBLE VERSE/STORY: _____

_____

_____

now I lay me down to sleep....

TONIGHT I PRAY FOR: _____

TONIGHT I THANK GOD FOR: _____

TONIGHT _____
  IS ON MY HEART

amen.

TODAY'S DATE: _____ S M T W Th F S

✗ ✗ ✗ ✗ ✗ ✗ ✗ ✗ ✗ ✗

DEAR GOD

TODAY I THANK YOU FOR:

1. _____

2. _____

3. _____

TODAY I ASK YOU FOR: _____

_____

TODAY I AM PRAYING FOR THESE PEOPLE:

1. _____

2. _____

3. _____

TODAY'S BIBLE VERSE/STORY: _____

_____

_____

now I lay me down to sleep....

TONIGHT I PRAY FOR: _____

TONIGHT I THANK GOD FOR: _____

TONIGHT _____
   IS ON MY HEART

amen.

TODAY'S DATE: _____ S M T W Th F S

✕ ✕ ✕ ✕ ✕ ✕ ✕ ✕ ✕ ✕ ✕

DEAR GOD

TODAY I THANK YOU FOR:

1. _____

2. _____

3. _____

TODAY I ASK YOU FOR: _____

_____

TODAY I AM PRAYING FOR THESE PEOPLE:

1. _____

2. _____

3. _____

TODAY'S BIBLE VERSE/STORY: _____

_____

_____

now I lay me down to sleep....

TONIGHT I PRAY FOR: _____

TONIGHT I THANK GOD FOR: _____

TONIGHT _____
      IS ON MY HEART

amen.

TODAY'S DATE: _____ S M T W Th F S

✗ ✗ ✗ ✗ ✗ ✗ ✗ ✗ ✗ ✗ ✗

DEAR GOD

TODAY I THANK YOU FOR:

1. _____

2. _____

3. _____

TODAY I ASK YOU FOR: _____

_____

TODAY I AM PRAYING FOR THESE PEOPLE:

1. _____

2. _____

3. _____

TODAY'S BIBLE VERSE/STORY: _____

_____

_____

now I lay me down to sleep....

TONIGHT I PRAY FOR: _____

TONIGHT I THANK GOD FOR: _____

TONIGHT _____
    IS ON MY HEART

amen.

TODAY'S DATE: _____ S M T W Th F S

✕ ✕ ✕ ✕ ✕ ✕ ✕ ✕ ✕ ✕ ✕

DEAR GOD

TODAY I THANK YOU FOR:

1. _____
2. _____
3. _____

TODAY I ASK YOU FOR: _____
_____

TODAY I AM PRAYING FOR THESE PEOPLE:

1. _____
2. _____
3. _____

TODAY'S BIBLE VERSE/STORY: _____
_____
_____

now I lay me down to sleep....

TONIGHT I PRAY FOR: _____

TONIGHT I THANK GOD FOR: _____

TONIGHT _____
   IS ON MY HEART

amen.

TODAY'S DATE: _____ S M T W Th F S

✕ ✕ ✕ ✕ ✕ ✕ ✕ ✕ ✕ ✕ ✕

DEAR GOD

TODAY I THANK YOU FOR:

1. _____

2. _____

3. _____

TODAY I ASK YOU FOR: _____

_____

TODAY I AM PRAYING FOR THESE PEOPLE:

1. _____

2. _____

3. _____

TODAY'S BIBLE VERSE/STORY: _____

_____

_____

now I lay me down to sleep....

TONIGHT I PRAY FOR: _____

TONIGHT I THANK GOD FOR: _____

TONIGHT _____
    IS ON MY HEART

amen.

TODAY'S DATE: _____   S M T W Th F S

✗ ✗ ✗ ✗ ✗ ✗ ✗ ✗ ✗ ✗ ✗

DEAR GOD

TODAY I THANK YOU FOR:

1. _____

2. _____

3. _____

TODAY I ASK YOU FOR: _____

_____

TODAY I AM PRAYING FOR THESE PEOPLE:

1. _____

2. _____

3. _____

TODAY'S BIBLE VERSE/STORY: _____

_____

_____

now I lay me down to sleep....

TONIGHT I PRAY FOR: _____

TONIGHT I THANK GOD FOR: _____

TONIGHT _____
  IS ON MY HEART

amen.

BE JOYFUL IN HOPE, PATIENT IN AFFLICTION, FAITHFUL IN PRAYER.

Romans 12:12

TODAY'S DATE: _____ S M T W Th F S

✕ ✕ ✕ ✕ ✕ ✕ ✕ ✕ ✕ ✕ ✕

DEAR GOD

TODAY I THANK YOU FOR:

    1. _____

    2. _____

    3. _____

TODAY I ASK YOU FOR: _____

_____

TODAY I AM PRAYING FOR THESE PEOPLE:

    1. _____

    2. _____

    3. _____

TODAY'S BIBLE VERSE/STORY: _____

_____

_____

now I lay me down to sleep....

TONIGHT I PRAY FOR: _____

TONIGHT I THANK GOD FOR: _____

TONIGHT _____
    IS ON MY HEART

amen.

TODAY'S DATE: _____ S M T W Th F S

✕ ✕ ✕ ✕ ✕ ✕ ✕ ✕ ✕ ✕ ✕

DEAR GOD

TODAY I THANK YOU FOR:

1. _____

2. _____

3. _____

TODAY I ASK YOU FOR: _____

_____

TODAY I AM PRAYING FOR THESE PEOPLE:

1. _____

2. _____

3. _____

TODAY'S BIBLE VERSE/STORY: _____

_____

_____

now I lay me down to sleep....

TONIGHT I PRAY FOR: _____

TONIGHT I THANK GOD FOR: _____

TONIGHT _____
   IS ON MY HEART

amen.

TODAY'S DATE: _____ S M T W Th F S

✗ ✗ ✗ ✗ ✗ ✗ ✗ ✗ ✗ ✗ ✗

DEAR GOD

TODAY I THANK YOU FOR:

1. _____

2. _____

3. _____

TODAY I ASK YOU FOR: _____

_____

TODAY I AM PRAYING FOR THESE PEOPLE:

1. _____

2. _____

3. _____

TODAY'S BIBLE VERSE/STORY: _____

_____

_____

now I lay me down to sleep....

TONIGHT I PRAY FOR: _____

TONIGHT I THANK GOD FOR: _____

TONIGHT _____
    IS ON MY HEART

amen.

TODAY'S DATE: _____ S M T W Th F S

✗ ✗ ✗ ✗ ✗ ✗ ✗ ✗ ✗ ✗ ✗

DEAR GOD

TODAY I THANK YOU FOR:

1. _____

2. _____

3. _____

TODAY I ASK YOU FOR: _____

_____

TODAY I AM PRAYING FOR THESE PEOPLE:

1. _____

2. _____

3. _____

TODAY'S BIBLE VERSE/STORY: _____

_____

_____

now I lay me down to sleep....

TONIGHT I PRAY FOR: _____

TONIGHT I THANK GOD FOR: _____

TONIGHT _____
    IS ON MY HEART

amen.

TODAY'S DATE: _____ S M T W Th F S

✗ ✗ ✗ ✗ ✗ ✗ ✗ ✗ ✗ ✗ ✗

DEAR GOD

TODAY I THANK YOU FOR:

1. _____

2. _____

3. _____

TODAY I ASK YOU FOR: _____

_____

TODAY I AM PRAYING FOR THESE PEOPLE:

1. _____

2. _____

3. _____

TODAY'S BIBLE VERSE/STORY: _____

_____

_____

now I lay me down to sleep....

TONIGHT I PRAY FOR: _____

TONIGHT I THANK GOD FOR: _____

TONIGHT _____
     IS ON MY HEART

amen.

TODAY'S DATE: _____ S M T W Th F S

✕ ✕ ✕ ✕ ✕ ✕ ✕ ✕ ✕ ✕ ✕

DEAR GOD

TODAY I THANK YOU FOR:

1. _____

2. _____

3. _____

TODAY I ASK YOU FOR: _____

_____

TODAY I AM PRAYING FOR THESE PEOPLE:

1. _____

2. _____

3. _____

TODAY'S BIBLE VERSE/STORY: _____

_____

_____

now I lay me down to sleep....

TONIGHT I PRAY FOR: _____

TONIGHT I THANK GOD FOR: _____

TONIGHT _____
    IS ON MY HEART

amen.

TODAY'S DATE: _____ S M T W Th F S

✕ ✕ ✕ ✕ ✕ ✕ ✕ ✕ ✕ ✕ ✕

DEAR GOD

TODAY I THANK YOU FOR:

　1. _____

　2. _____

　3. _____

TODAY I ASK YOU FOR: _____

_____

TODAY I AM PRAYING FOR THESE PEOPLE:

　1. _____

　2. _____

　3. _____

TODAY'S BIBLE VERSE/STORY: _____

_____

_____

now I lay me down to sleep....

TONIGHT I PRAY FOR: _____

TONIGHT I THANK GOD FOR: _____

TONIGHT _____
　　IS ON MY HEART

amen.

TODAY'S DATE: _____ S M T W Th F S

× × × × × × × × × × ×

DEAR GOD

TODAY I THANK YOU FOR:

1. _____

2. _____

3. _____

TODAY I ASK YOU FOR: _____

_____

TODAY I AM PRAYING FOR THESE PEOPLE:

1. _____

2. _____

3. _____

TODAY'S BIBLE VERSE/STORY: _____

_____

_____

now I lay me down to sleep....

TONIGHT I PRAY FOR: _____

TONIGHT I THANK GOD FOR: _____

TONIGHT _____
    IS ON MY HEART

amen.

CAST ALL YOUR ANXIETY ON HIM BECAUSE HE CARES FOR YOU.

1 Peter 5:7

TODAY'S DATE: _____ S M T W Th F S

x x x x x x x x x x x

DEAR GOD

TODAY I THANK YOU FOR:

1. _____

2. _____

3. _____

TODAY I ASK YOU FOR: _____

_____

TODAY I AM PRAYING FOR THESE PEOPLE:

1. _____

2. _____

3. _____

TODAY'S BIBLE VERSE/STORY: _____

_____

_____

now I lay me down to sleep....

TONIGHT I PRAY FOR: _____

TONIGHT I THANK GOD FOR: _____

TONIGHT _____
    IS ON MY HEART

amen.

TODAY'S DATE: _____ S M T W Th F S

✕ ✕ ✕ ✕ ✕ ✕ ✕ ✕ ✕ ✕ ✕

DEAR GOD

TODAY I THANK YOU FOR:

1. _____

2. _____

3. _____

TODAY I ASK YOU FOR: _____

_____

TODAY I AM PRAYING FOR THESE PEOPLE:

1. _____

2. _____

3. _____

TODAY'S BIBLE VERSE/STORY: _____

_____

_____

now I lay me down to sleep....

TONIGHT I PRAY FOR: _____

TONIGHT I THANK GOD FOR: _____

TONIGHT _____
     IS ON MY HEART

amen.

TODAY'S DATE: _____ S M T W Th F S

✕ ✕ ✕ ✕ ✕ ✕ ✕ ✕ ✕ ✕ ✕

DEAR GOD

TODAY I THANK YOU FOR:

1. _____

2. _____

3. _____

TODAY I ASK YOU FOR: _____

_____

TODAY I AM PRAYING FOR THESE PEOPLE:

1. _____

2. _____

3. _____

TODAY'S BIBLE VERSE/STORY: _____

_____

_____

now I lay me down to sleep....

TONIGHT I PRAY FOR: _____

TONIGHT I THANK GOD FOR: _____

TONIGHT _____
  IS ON MY HEART

amen.

TODAY'S DATE: _____ S M T W Th F S

✕ ✕ ✕ ✕ ✕ ✕ ✕ ✕ ✕ ✕ ✕

DEAR GOD

TODAY I THANK YOU FOR:

   1. _____

   2. _____

   3. _____

TODAY I ASK YOU FOR: _____

_____

TODAY I AM PRAYING FOR THESE PEOPLE:

   1. _____

   2. _____

   3. _____

TODAY'S BIBLE VERSE/STORY: _____

_____

_____

now I lay me down to sleep....

TONIGHT I PRAY FOR: _____

TONIGHT I THANK GOD FOR: _____

TONIGHT _____
   IS ON MY HEART

amen.

TODAY'S DATE: _____   S M T W Th F S

✕ ✕ ✕ ✕ ✕ ✕ ✕ ✕ ✕ ✕ ✕

DEAR GOD

TODAY I THANK YOU FOR:

1. _____

2. _____

3. _____

TODAY I ASK YOU FOR: _____

_____

TODAY I AM PRAYING FOR THESE PEOPLE:

1. _____

2. _____

3. _____

TODAY'S BIBLE VERSE/STORY: _____

_____

_____

now I lay me down to sleep....

TONIGHT I PRAY FOR: _____

TONIGHT I THANK GOD FOR: _____

TONIGHT _____
    IS ON MY HEART

amen.

TODAY'S DATE: _____ S M T W Th F S

✕ ✕ ✕ ✕ ✕ ✕ ✕ ✕ ✕ ✕ ✕

DEAR GOD

TODAY I THANK YOU FOR:

1. _____
2. _____
3. _____

TODAY I ASK YOU FOR: _____
_____

TODAY I AM PRAYING FOR THESE PEOPLE:

1. _____
2. _____
3. _____

TODAY'S BIBLE VERSE/STORY: _____
_____
_____

now I lay me down to sleep....

TONIGHT I PRAY FOR: _____

TONIGHT I THANK GOD FOR: _____

TONIGHT _____
   IS ON MY HEART

amen.

TODAY'S DATE: _____ S M T W Th F S

✗ ✗ ✗ ✗ ✗ ✗ ✗ ✗ ✗ ✗ ✗

DEAR GOD

TODAY I THANK YOU FOR:

1. _____
2. _____
3. _____

TODAY I ASK YOU FOR: _____
_____

TODAY I AM PRAYING FOR THESE PEOPLE:

1. _____
2. _____
3. _____

TODAY'S BIBLE VERSE/STORY: _____
_____
_____

now I lay me down to sleep....

TONIGHT I PRAY FOR: _____

TONIGHT I THANK GOD FOR: _____

TONIGHT _____
   IS ON MY HEART

amen.

TODAY'S DATE: _____ S M T W Th F S

✕ ✕ ✕ ✕ ✕ ✕ ✕ ✕ ✕ ✕ ✕

DEAR GOD

TODAY I THANK YOU FOR:

1. _____

2. _____

3. _____

TODAY I ASK YOU FOR: _____

_____

TODAY I AM PRAYING FOR THESE PEOPLE:

1. _____

2. _____

3. _____

TODAY'S BIBLE VERSE/STORY: _____

_____

_____

now I lay me down to sleep....

TONIGHT I PRAY FOR: _____

TONIGHT I THANK GOD FOR: _____

TONIGHT _____
    IS ON MY HEART

amen.

LOOK TO THE LORD AND HIS STRENGTH; SEEK HIS FACE ALWAYS.

1 Chronicles 16:11

TODAY'S DATE: _____ S M T W Th F S

✗ ✗ ✗ ✗ ✗ ✗ ✗ ✗ ✗ ✗ ✗

TODAY I THANK YOU FOR:

1. _____
2. _____
3. _____

TODAY I ASK YOU FOR: _____

_____

TODAY I AM PRAYING FOR THESE PEOPLE:

1. _____
2. _____
3. _____

TODAY'S BIBLE VERSE/STORY: _____

_____

_____

now I lay me down to sleep....

TONIGHT I PRAY FOR: _____

TONIGHT I THANK GOD FOR: _____

TONIGHT _____
   IS ON MY HEART

amen.

TODAY'S DATE: _____ S M T W Th F S

✗ ✗ ✗ ✗ ✗ ✗ ✗ ✗ ✗ ✗ ✗

DEAR GOD

TODAY I THANK YOU FOR:

1. _____

2. _____

3. _____

TODAY I ASK YOU FOR: _____

_____

TODAY I AM PRAYING FOR THESE PEOPLE:

1. _____

2. _____

3. _____

TODAY'S BIBLE VERSE/STORY: _____

_____

_____

now I lay me down to sleep....

TONIGHT I PRAY FOR: _____

TONIGHT I THANK GOD FOR: _____

TONIGHT _____
   IS ON MY HEART

amen.

TODAY'S DATE: _____ S M T W Th F S

✕ ✕ ✕ ✕ ✕ ✕ ✕ ✕ ✕ ✕

TODAY I THANK YOU FOR:

DEAR GOD

   1. _____

   2. _____

   3. _____

TODAY I ASK YOU FOR: _____

_____

TODAY I AM PRAYING FOR THESE PEOPLE:

   1. _____

   2. _____

   3. _____

TODAY'S BIBLE VERSE/STORY: _____

_____

_____

now I lay me down to sleep....

TONIGHT I PRAY FOR: _____

TONIGHT I THANK GOD FOR: _____

TONIGHT _____
   IS ON MY HEART

amen.

TODAY'S DATE: _____ S M T W Th F S

✗ ✗ ✗ ✗ ✗ ✗ ✗ ✗ ✗ ✗ ✗ ✗

DEAR GOD

TODAY I THANK YOU FOR:

1. _____

2. _____

3. _____

TODAY I ASK YOU FOR: _____

_____

TODAY I AM PRAYING FOR THESE PEOPLE:

1. _____

2. _____

3. _____

TODAY'S BIBLE VERSE/STORY: _____

_____

_____

now I lay me down to sleep....

TONIGHT I PRAY FOR: _____

TONIGHT I THANK GOD FOR: _____

TONIGHT _____
   IS ON MY HEART

amen.

TODAY'S DATE: _____ S M T W Th F S

✕ ✕ ✕ ✕ ✕ ✕ ✕ ✕ ✕ ✕ ✕

DEAR GOD

TODAY I THANK YOU FOR:

1. _____

2. _____

3. _____

TODAY I ASK YOU FOR: _____

_____

TODAY I AM PRAYING FOR THESE PEOPLE:

1. _____

2. _____

3. _____

TODAY'S BIBLE VERSE/STORY: _____

_____

_____

now I lay me down to sleep....

TONIGHT I PRAY FOR: _____

TONIGHT I THANK GOD FOR: _____

TONIGHT _____
   IS ON MY HEART

amen.

TODAY'S DATE: _____ S M T W Th F S

✗ ✗ ✗ ✗ ✗ ✗ ✗ ✗ ✗ ✗ ✗

DEAR GOD

TODAY I THANK YOU FOR:

1. _____

2. _____

3. _____

TODAY I ASK YOU FOR: _____

_____

TODAY I AM PRAYING FOR THESE PEOPLE:

1. _____

2. _____

3. _____

TODAY'S BIBLE VERSE/STORY: _____

_____

_____

now I lay me down to sleep....

TONIGHT I PRAY FOR: _____

TONIGHT I THANK GOD FOR: _____

TONIGHT _____
    IS ON MY HEART

amen.

TODAY'S DATE: _____ S M T W Th F S

✗ ✗ ✗ ✗ ✗ ✗ ✗ ✗ ✗ ✗ ✗

DEAR GOD

TODAY I THANK YOU FOR:

1. _____

2. _____

3. _____

TODAY I ASK YOU FOR: _____

_____

TODAY I AM PRAYING FOR THESE PEOPLE:

1. _____

2. _____

3. _____

TODAY'S BIBLE VERSE/STORY: _____

_____

_____

now I lay me down to sleep....

TONIGHT I PRAY FOR: _____

TONIGHT I THANK GOD FOR: _____

TONIGHT _____
     IS ON MY HEART

amen.

TODAY'S DATE: _____ S M T W Th F S

✗ ✗ ✗ ✗ ✗ ✗ ✗ ✗ ✗ ✗ ✗

DEAR GOD

TODAY I THANK YOU FOR:

1. _____

2. _____

3. _____

TODAY I ASK YOU FOR: _____

_____

TODAY I AM PRAYING FOR THESE PEOPLE:

1. _____

2. _____

3. _____

TODAY'S BIBLE VERSE/STORY: _____

_____

_____

now I lay me down to sleep....

TONIGHT I PRAY FOR: _____

TONIGHT I THANK GOD FOR: _____

TONIGHT _____
    IS ON MY HEART

amen.

BE STILL & KNOW THAT I AM GOD.

Psalm 46:10

TODAY'S DATE: _____ S M T W Th F S

✗ ✗ ✗ ✗ ✗ ✗ ✗ ✗ ✗ ✗ ✗

DEAR GOD

TODAY I THANK YOU FOR:

1. _____

2. _____

3. _____

TODAY I ASK YOU FOR: _____

_____

TODAY I AM PRAYING FOR THESE PEOPLE:

1. _____

2. _____

3. _____

TODAY'S BIBLE VERSE/STORY: _____

_____

_____

now I lay me down to sleep....

TONIGHT I PRAY FOR: _____

TONIGHT I THANK GOD FOR: _____

TONIGHT _____
    IS ON MY HEART

amen.

TODAY'S DATE: _____ S M T W Th F S

✗ ✗ ✗ ✗ ✗ ✗ ✗ ✗ ✗ ✗ ✗

DEAR GOD

TODAY I THANK YOU FOR:

1. _____

2. _____

3. _____

TODAY I ASK YOU FOR: _____

_____

TODAY I AM PRAYING FOR THESE PEOPLE:

1. _____

2. _____

3. _____

TODAY'S BIBLE VERSE/STORY: _____

_____

_____

now I lay me down to sleep....

TONIGHT I PRAY FOR: _____

TONIGHT I THANK GOD FOR: _____

TONIGHT _____
    IS ON MY HEART

amen.

TODAY'S DATE: _____ S M T W Th F S

✗ ✗ ✗ ✗ ✗ ✗ ✗ ✗ ✗ ✗ ✗

DEAR GOD

TODAY I THANK YOU FOR:

   1. _____

   2. _____

   3. _____

TODAY I ASK YOU FOR: _____

_____

TODAY I AM PRAYING FOR THESE PEOPLE:

   1. _____

   2. _____

   3. _____

TODAY'S BIBLE VERSE/STORY: _____

_____

_____

now I lay me down to sleep....

TONIGHT I PRAY FOR: _____

TONIGHT I THANK GOD FOR: _____

TONIGHT _____
   IS ON MY HEART

amen.

TODAY'S DATE: _____ S M T W Th F S

✗ ✗ ✗ ✗ ✗ ✗ ✗ ✗ ✗ ✗ ✗

TODAY I THANK YOU FOR:

DEAR GOD

1. _____

2. _____

3. _____

TODAY I ASK YOU FOR: _____

_____

TODAY I AM PRAYING FOR THESE PEOPLE:

1. _____

2. _____

3. _____

TODAY'S BIBLE VERSE/STORY: _____

_____

_____

now I lay me down to sleep....

TONIGHT I PRAY FOR: _____

TONIGHT I THANK GOD FOR: _____

TONIGHT _____
    IS ON MY HEART

amen.

TODAY'S DATE: _____ S M T W Th F S

✗ ✗ ✗ ✗ ✗ ✗ ✗ ✗ ✗ ✗ ✗

DEAR GOD

TODAY I THANK YOU FOR:

1. _____

2. _____

3. _____

TODAY I ASK YOU FOR: _____

_____

TODAY I AM PRAYING FOR THESE PEOPLE:

1. _____

2. _____

3. _____

TODAY'S BIBLE VERSE/STORY: _____

_____

_____

now I lay me down to sleep....

TONIGHT I PRAY FOR: _____

TONIGHT I THANK GOD FOR: _____

TONIGHT _____
   IS ON MY HEART

amen.

TODAY'S DATE: _____ S M T W Th F S

✗ ✗ ✗ ✗ ✗ ✗ ✗ ✗ ✗ ✗ ✗

DEAR GOD

TODAY I THANK YOU FOR:

1. _____

2. _____

3. _____

TODAY I ASK YOU FOR: _____

_____

TODAY I AM PRAYING FOR THESE PEOPLE:

1. _____

2. _____

3. _____

TODAY'S BIBLE VERSE/STORY: _____

_____

_____

now I lay me down to sleep....

TONIGHT I PRAY FOR: _____

TONIGHT I THANK GOD FOR: _____

TONIGHT _____
   IS ON MY HEART

amen.

TODAY'S DATE: _____ S M T W Th F S

× × × × × × × × × × ×

DEAR GOD

TODAY I THANK YOU FOR:

1. _____
2. _____
3. _____

TODAY I ASK YOU FOR: _____

_____

TODAY I AM PRAYING FOR THESE PEOPLE:

1. _____
2. _____
3. _____

TODAY'S BIBLE VERSE/STORY: _____

_____

_____

now I lay me down to sleep....

TONIGHT I PRAY FOR: _____

TONIGHT I THANK GOD FOR: _____

TONIGHT _____
    IS ON MY HEART

amen.

TODAY'S DATE: _____ S M T W Th F S

✗ ✗ ✗ ✗ ✗ ✗ ✗ ✗ ✗ ✗ ✗

DEAR GOD

TODAY I THANK YOU FOR:

1. _____

2. _____

3. _____

TODAY I ASK YOU FOR: _____

_____

TODAY I AM PRAYING FOR THESE PEOPLE:

1. _____

2. _____

3. _____

TODAY'S BIBLE VERSE/STORY: _____

_____

_____

now I lay me down to sleep....

TONIGHT I PRAY FOR: _____

TONIGHT I THANK GOD FOR: _____

TONIGHT _____
   IS ON MY HEART

amen.

TODAY'S DATE: _____ S M T W Th F S

× × × × × × × × × × ×

DEAR GOD

TODAY I THANK YOU FOR:

1. _____
2. _____
3. _____

TODAY I ASK YOU FOR: _____

_____

TODAY I AM PRAYING FOR THESE PEOPLE:

1. _____
2. _____
3. _____

TODAY'S BIBLE VERSE/STORY: _____

_____

_____

now I lay me down to sleep....

TONIGHT I PRAY FOR: _____

TONIGHT I THANK GOD FOR: _____

TONIGHT _____
     IS ON MY HEART

amen.

TODAY'S DATE: _____ S M T W Th F S

✗ ✗ ✗ ✗ ✗ ✗ ✗ ✗ ✗ ✗ ✗

DEAR GOD

TODAY I THANK YOU FOR:

1. _____

2. _____

3. _____

TODAY I ASK YOU FOR: _____

_____

TODAY I AM PRAYING FOR THESE PEOPLE:

1. _____

2. _____

3. _____

TODAY'S BIBLE VERSE/STORY: _____

_____

_____

now I lay me down to sleep....

TONIGHT I PRAY FOR: _____

TONIGHT I THANK GOD FOR: _____

TONIGHT _____

IS ON MY HEART

amen.

GIVE, AND IT WILL BE GIVEN TO YOU.

Luke 6:38

TODAY'S DATE: _____ S M T W Th F S

✗ ✗ ✗ ✗ ✗ ✗ ✗ ✗ ✗ ✗

DEAR GOD

TODAY I THANK YOU FOR:

1. _____

2. _____

3. _____

TODAY I ASK YOU FOR: _____

_____

TODAY I AM PRAYING FOR THESE PEOPLE:

1. _____

2. _____

3. _____

TODAY'S BIBLE VERSE/STORY: _____

_____

_____

now I lay me down to sleep....

TONIGHT I PRAY FOR: _____

TONIGHT I THANK GOD FOR: _____

TONIGHT _____
    IS ON MY HEART

amen.

TODAY'S DATE: _____ S M T W Th F S

✕ ✕ ✕ ✕ ✕ ✕ ✕ ✕ ✕ ✕ ✕

DEAR GOD

TODAY I THANK YOU FOR:

1. _____

2. _____

3. _____

TODAY I ASK YOU FOR: _____

_____

TODAY I AM PRAYING FOR THESE PEOPLE:

1. _____

2. _____

3. _____

TODAY'S BIBLE VERSE/STORY: _____

_____

_____

now I lay me down to sleep....

TONIGHT I PRAY FOR: _____

TONIGHT I THANK GOD FOR: _____

TONIGHT _____
    IS ON MY HEART

amen.

TODAY'S DATE: _____ S M T W Th F S

✕ ✕ ✕ ✕ ✕ ✕ ✕ ✕ ✕ ✕ ✕

TODAY I THANK YOU FOR:

DEAR GOD

1. _____

2. _____

3. _____

TODAY I ASK YOU FOR: _____

_____

TODAY I AM PRAYING FOR THESE PEOPLE:

1. _____

2. _____

3. _____

TODAY'S BIBLE VERSE/STORY: _____

_____

_____

now I lay me down to sleep....

TONIGHT I PRAY FOR: _____

TONIGHT I THANK GOD FOR: _____

TONIGHT _____
   IS ON MY HEART

amen.

TODAY'S DATE: _____ S M T W Th F S

✕ ✕ ✕ ✕ ✕ ✕ ✕ ✕ ✕ ✕

DEAR GOD

TODAY I THANK YOU FOR:

1. _____
2. _____
3. _____

TODAY I ASK YOU FOR: _____

_____

TODAY I AM PRAYING FOR THESE PEOPLE:

1. _____
2. _____
3. _____

TODAY'S BIBLE VERSE/STORY: _____

_____

_____

now I lay me down to sleep....

TONIGHT I PRAY FOR: _____

TONIGHT I THANK GOD FOR: _____

TONIGHT _____
    IS ON MY HEART

amen.

TODAY'S DATE: _____ S M T W Th F S

✕ ✕ ✕ ✕ ✕ ✕ ✕ ✕ ✕ ✕ ✕

DEAR GOD

TODAY I THANK YOU FOR:

1. _____
2. _____
3. _____

TODAY I ASK YOU FOR: _____

_____

TODAY I AM PRAYING FOR THESE PEOPLE:

1. _____
2. _____
3. _____

TODAY'S BIBLE VERSE/STORY: _____

_____

_____

now I lay me down to sleep....

TONIGHT I PRAY FOR: _____

TONIGHT I THANK GOD FOR: _____

TONIGHT _____
    IS ON MY HEART

amen.

TODAY'S DATE: _____ S M T W Th F S

✗ ✗ ✗ ✗ ✗ ✗ ✗ ✗ ✗ ✗ ✗

DEAR GOD

TODAY I THANK YOU FOR:

1. _____

2. _____

3. _____

TODAY I ASK YOU FOR: _____

_____

TODAY I AM PRAYING FOR THESE PEOPLE:

1. _____

2. _____

3. _____

TODAY'S BIBLE VERSE/STORY: _____

_____

_____

now I lay me down to sleep....

TONIGHT I PRAY FOR: _____

TONIGHT I THANK GOD FOR: _____

TONIGHT _____
    IS ON MY HEART

amen.

TODAY'S DATE: _____   S M T W Th F S

✕ ✕ ✕ ✕ ✕ ✕ ✕ ✕ ✕ ✕ ✕

DEAR GOD

TODAY I THANK YOU FOR:

1. _____
2. _____
3. _____

TODAY I ASK YOU FOR: _____

_____

TODAY I AM PRAYING FOR THESE PEOPLE:

1. _____
2. _____
3. _____

TODAY'S BIBLE VERSE/STORY: _____

_____

_____

now I lay me down to sleep....

TONIGHT I PRAY FOR: _____

TONIGHT I THANK GOD FOR: _____

TONIGHT _____
     IS ON MY HEART

amen.

TODAY'S DATE: _____ S M T W Th F S

✕ ✕ ✕ ✕ ✕ ✕ ✕ ✕ ✕ ✕ ✕

DEAR GOD

TODAY I THANK YOU FOR:

1. _____

2. _____

3. _____

TODAY I ASK YOU FOR: _____

_____

TODAY I AM PRAYING FOR THESE PEOPLE:

1. _____

2. _____

3. _____

TODAY'S BIBLE VERSE/STORY: _____

_____

_____

now I lay me down to sleep....

TONIGHT I PRAY FOR: _____

TONIGHT I THANK GOD FOR: _____

TONIGHT _____
    IS ON MY HEART

amen.

SET YOUR MIND ON THINGS ABOVE.

Colossians 3:2

TODAY'S DATE: _____ S M T W Th F S

✗ ✗ ✗ ✗ ✗ ✗ ✗ ✗ ✗ ✗ ✗

DEAR GOD

TODAY I THANK YOU FOR:

1. _____

2. _____

3. _____

TODAY I ASK YOU FOR: _____

_____

TODAY I AM PRAYING FOR THESE PEOPLE:

1. _____

2. _____

3. _____

TODAY'S BIBLE VERSE/STORY: _____

_____

_____

now I lay me down to sleep....

TONIGHT I PRAY FOR: _____

TONIGHT I THANK GOD FOR: _____

TONIGHT _____
    IS ON MY HEART

amen.

TODAY'S DATE: _____ S M T W Th F S

✗ ✗ ✗ ✗ ✗ ✗ ✗ ✗ ✗ ✗ ✗

DEAR GOD

TODAY I THANK YOU FOR:

1. _____

2. _____

3. _____

TODAY I ASK YOU FOR: _____

_____

TODAY I AM PRAYING FOR THESE PEOPLE:

1. _____

2. _____

3. _____

TODAY'S BIBLE VERSE/STORY: _____

_____

_____

now I lay me down to sleep....

TONIGHT I PRAY FOR: _____

TONIGHT I THANK GOD FOR: _____

TONIGHT _____
    IS ON MY HEART

amen.

TODAY'S DATE: _____ S M T W Th F S

✗ ✗ ✗ ✗ ✗ ✗ ✗ ✗ ✗ ✗ ✗ **DEAR GOD**

TODAY I THANK YOU FOR:

1. _____

2. _____

3. _____

TODAY I ASK YOU FOR: _____

_____

TODAY I AM PRAYING FOR THESE PEOPLE:

1. _____

2. _____

3. _____

TODAY'S BIBLE VERSE/STORY: _____

_____

_____

now I lay me down to sleep....

TONIGHT I PRAY FOR: _____

TONIGHT I THANK GOD FOR: _____

TONIGHT _____
    IS ON MY HEART

amen.

TODAY'S DATE: _____ S M T W Th F S

✕ ✕ ✕ ✕ ✕ ✕ ✕ ✕ ✕ ✕ ✕

TODAY I THANK YOU FOR:

DEAR GOD

1. _____

2. _____

3. _____

TODAY I ASK YOU FOR: _____

_____

TODAY I AM PRAYING FOR THESE PEOPLE:

1. _____

2. _____

3. _____

TODAY'S BIBLE VERSE/STORY: _____

_____

_____

now I lay me down to sleep....

TONIGHT I PRAY FOR: _____

TONIGHT I THANK GOD FOR: _____

TONIGHT _____
    IS ON MY HEART

amen.

TODAY'S DATE: _____ S M T W Th F S

× × × × × × × × × × ×

DEAR GOD

TODAY I THANK YOU FOR:

1. _____

2. _____

3. _____

TODAY I ASK YOU FOR: _____

_____

TODAY I AM PRAYING FOR THESE PEOPLE:

1. _____

2. _____

3. _____

TODAY'S BIBLE VERSE/STORY: _____

_____

_____

now I lay me down to sleep....

TONIGHT I PRAY FOR: _____

TONIGHT I THANK GOD FOR: _____

TONIGHT _____
    IS ON MY HEART

amen.

TODAY'S DATE: _____ S M T W Th F S

X X X X X X X X X X X

DEAR GOD

TODAY I THANK YOU FOR:

1. _____

2. _____

3. _____

TODAY I ASK YOU FOR: _____

_____

TODAY I AM PRAYING FOR THESE PEOPLE:

1. _____

2. _____

3. _____

TODAY'S BIBLE VERSE/STORY: _____

_____

_____

now I lay me down to sleep....

TONIGHT I PRAY FOR: _____

TONIGHT I THANK GOD FOR: _____

TONIGHT _____
   IS ON MY HEART

amen.

TODAY'S DATE: _____ S M T W Th F S

× × × × × × × × × × ×

DEAR GOD

TODAY I THANK YOU FOR:

1. _____
2. _____
3. _____

TODAY I ASK YOU FOR: _____

_____

TODAY I AM PRAYING FOR THESE PEOPLE:

1. _____
2. _____
3. _____

TODAY'S BIBLE VERSE/STORY: _____

_____

_____

now I lay me down to sleep....

TONIGHT I PRAY FOR: _____

TONIGHT I THANK GOD FOR: _____

TONIGHT _____
    IS ON MY HEART

amen.

TODAY'S DATE: _____ S M T W Th F S

× × × × × × × × × × ×

DEAR GOD

TODAY I THANK YOU FOR:

1. _____

2. _____

3. _____

TODAY I ASK YOU FOR: _____

_____

TODAY I AM PRAYING FOR THESE PEOPLE:

1. _____

2. _____

3. _____

TODAY'S BIBLE VERSE/STORY: _____

_____

_____

now I lay me down to sleep....

TONIGHT I PRAY FOR: _____

TONIGHT I THANK GOD FOR: _____

TONIGHT _____
    IS ON MY HEART

amen.

I CAN DO ALL THINGS THROUGH CHRIST WHO STRENGTHENS ME.

Philippians 4:13

TODAY'S DATE: _____ S M T W Th F S

✕ ✕ ✕ ✕ ✕ ✕ ✕ ✕ ✕ ✕

DEAR GOD

TODAY I THANK YOU FOR:

1. _____

2. _____

3. _____

TODAY I ASK YOU FOR: _____

_____

TODAY I AM PRAYING FOR THESE PEOPLE:

1. _____

2. _____

3. _____

TODAY'S BIBLE VERSE/STORY: _____

_____

_____

now I lay me down to sleep....

TONIGHT I PRAY FOR: _____

TONIGHT I THANK GOD FOR: _____

TONIGHT _____
   IS ON MY HEART

amen.

TODAY'S DATE: _____ S M T W Th F S

× × × × × × × × × × ×

DEAR GOD

TODAY I THANK YOU FOR:

1. _____

2. _____

3. _____

TODAY I ASK YOU FOR: _____

_____

TODAY I AM PRAYING FOR THESE PEOPLE:

1. _____

2. _____

3. _____

TODAY'S BIBLE VERSE/STORY: _____

_____

_____

now I lay me down to sleep....

TONIGHT I PRAY FOR: _____

TONIGHT I THANK GOD FOR: _____

TONIGHT _____
    IS ON MY HEART

amen.

TODAY'S DATE: _____ S M T W Th F S

✗ ✗ ✗ ✗ ✗ ✗ ✗ ✗ ✗ ✗ ✗

TODAY I THANK YOU FOR:

DEAR GOD

1. _____

2. _____

3. _____

TODAY I ASK YOU FOR: _____

_____

TODAY I AM PRAYING FOR THESE PEOPLE:

1. _____

2. _____

3. _____

TODAY'S BIBLE VERSE/STORY: _____

_____

_____

now I lay me down to sleep....

TONIGHT I PRAY FOR: _____

TONIGHT I THANK GOD FOR: _____

TONIGHT _____
   IS ON MY HEART

amen.

TODAY'S DATE: _____ S M T W Th F S

✕ ✕ ✕ ✕ ✕ ✕ ✕ ✕ ✕ ✕ ✕

DEAR GOD

TODAY I THANK YOU FOR:

1. _____

2. _____

3. _____

TODAY I ASK YOU FOR: _____

_____

TODAY I AM PRAYING FOR THESE PEOPLE:

1. _____

2. _____

3. _____

TODAY'S BIBLE VERSE/STORY: _____

_____

_____

now I lay me down to sleep....

TONIGHT I PRAY FOR: _____

TONIGHT I THANK GOD FOR: _____

TONIGHT _____
    IS ON MY HEART

amen.

TODAY'S DATE: _____ S M T W Th F S

✕ ✕ ✕ ✕ ✕ ✕ ✕ ✕ ✕ ✕ ✕

DEAR GOD

TODAY I THANK YOU FOR:

1. _____

2. _____

3. _____

TODAY I ASK YOU FOR: _____

_____

TODAY I AM PRAYING FOR THESE PEOPLE:

1. _____

2. _____

3. _____

TODAY'S BIBLE VERSE/STORY: _____

_____

_____

now I lay me down to sleep....

TONIGHT I PRAY FOR: _____

TONIGHT I THANK GOD FOR: _____

TONIGHT _____
    IS ON MY HEART

amen.

TODAY'S DATE: _____ S M T W Th F S

✗ ✗ ✗ ✗ ✗ ✗ ✗ ✗ ✗ ✗

DEAR GOD

TODAY I THANK YOU FOR:

1. _____

2. _____

3. _____

TODAY I ASK YOU FOR: _____

_____

TODAY I AM PRAYING FOR THESE PEOPLE:

1. _____

2. _____

3. _____

TODAY'S BIBLE VERSE/STORY: _____

_____

_____

now I lay me down to sleep....

TONIGHT I PRAY FOR: _____

TONIGHT I THANK GOD FOR: _____

TONIGHT _____
    IS ON MY HEART

amen.

TODAY'S DATE: _____ S M T W Th F S

✗ ✗ ✗ ✗ ✗ ✗ ✗ ✗ ✗ ✗ ✗

TODAY I THANK YOU FOR:

DEAR GOD

  1. _____

  2. _____

  3. _____

TODAY I ASK YOU FOR: _____

_____

TODAY I AM PRAYING FOR THESE PEOPLE:

  1. _____

  2. _____

  3. _____

TODAY'S BIBLE VERSE/STORY: _____

_____

_____

now I lay me down to sleep....

TONIGHT I PRAY FOR: _____

TONIGHT I THANK GOD FOR: _____

TONIGHT _____
   IS ON MY HEART

amen.

TODAY'S DATE: _____ S M T W Th F S

✗ ✗ ✗ ✗ ✗ ✗ ✗ ✗ ✗ ✗ ✗ ✗

DEAR GOD

TODAY I THANK YOU FOR:

1. _____

2. _____

3. _____

TODAY I ASK YOU FOR: _____

_____

TODAY I AM PRAYING FOR THESE PEOPLE:

1. _____

2. _____

3. _____

TODAY'S BIBLE VERSE/STORY: _____

_____

_____

now I lay me down to sleep....

TONIGHT I PRAY FOR: _____

TONIGHT I THANK GOD FOR: _____

TONIGHT _____
   IS ON MY HEART

amen.

BE KIND TO ONE ANOTHER.

Ephesians 4:32

TODAY'S DATE: _____   S M T W Th F S

✕ ✕ ✕ ✕ ✕ ✕ ✕ ✕ ✕ ✕ ✕

DEAR GOD

TODAY I THANK YOU FOR:

1. _____

2. _____

3. _____

TODAY I ASK YOU FOR: _____

_____

TODAY I AM PRAYING FOR THESE PEOPLE:

1. _____

2. _____

3. _____

TODAY'S BIBLE VERSE/STORY: _____

_____

_____

now I lay me down to sleep....

TONIGHT I PRAY FOR: _____

TONIGHT I THANK GOD FOR: _____

TONIGHT _____
    IS ON MY HEART

amen.

TODAY'S DATE: _____ S M T W Th F S

✕ ✕ ✕ ✕ ✕ ✕ ✕ ✕ ✕ ✕ ✕

DEAR GOD

TODAY I THANK YOU FOR:

1. _____

2. _____

3. _____

TODAY I ASK YOU FOR: _____

_____

TODAY I AM PRAYING FOR THESE PEOPLE:

1. _____

2. _____

3. _____

TODAY'S BIBLE VERSE/STORY: _____

_____

_____

now I lay me down to sleep....

TONIGHT I PRAY FOR: _____

TONIGHT I THANK GOD FOR: _____

TONIGHT _____
    IS ON MY HEART

amen.

TODAY'S DATE: _____ S M T W Th F S

✗ ✗ ✗ ✗ ✗ ✗ ✗ ✗ ✗ ✗ ✗

DEAR GOD

TODAY I THANK YOU FOR:

1. _____

2. _____

3. _____

TODAY I ASK YOU FOR: _____

_____

TODAY I AM PRAYING FOR THESE PEOPLE:

1. _____

2. _____

3. _____

TODAY'S BIBLE VERSE/STORY: _____

_____

_____

now I lay me down to sleep....

TONIGHT I PRAY FOR: _____

TONIGHT I THANK GOD FOR: _____

TONIGHT _____
IS ON MY HEART

amen.

TODAY'S DATE: _____ S M T W Th F S

✕ ✕ ✕ ✕ ✕ ✕ ✕ ✕ ✕ ✕

DEAR GOD

TODAY I THANK YOU FOR:

1. _____

2. _____

3. _____

TODAY I ASK YOU FOR: _____

_____

TODAY I AM PRAYING FOR THESE PEOPLE:

1. _____

2. _____

3. _____

TODAY'S BIBLE VERSE/STORY: _____

_____

_____

now I lay me down to sleep....

TONIGHT I PRAY FOR: _____

TONIGHT I THANK GOD FOR: _____

TONIGHT _____
   IS ON MY HEART

amen.

TODAY'S DATE: _____ S M T W Th F S

✕ ✕ ✕ ✕ ✕ ✕ ✕ ✕ ✕ ✕ ✕   DEAR GOD

TODAY I THANK YOU FOR:

   1. _____

   2. _____

   3. _____

TODAY I ASK YOU FOR: _____

_____

TODAY I AM PRAYING FOR THESE PEOPLE:

   1. _____

   2. _____

   3. _____

TODAY'S BIBLE VERSE/STORY: _____

_____

_____

now I lay me down to sleep....

TONIGHT I PRAY FOR: _____

TONIGHT I THANK GOD FOR: _____

TONIGHT _____
   IS ON MY HEART   amen.

TODAY'S DATE: _____ S M T W Th F S

× × × × × × × × × × ×

DEAR GOD

TODAY I THANK YOU FOR:

   1. _____

   2. _____

   3. _____

TODAY I ASK YOU FOR: _____

_____

TODAY I AM PRAYING FOR THESE PEOPLE:

   1. _____

   2. _____

   3. _____

TODAY'S BIBLE VERSE/STORY: _____

_____

_____

now I lay me down to sleep....

TONIGHT I PRAY FOR: _____

TONIGHT I THANK GOD FOR: _____

TONIGHT _____
   IS ON MY HEART

amen.

TODAY'S DATE: _____ S M T W Th F S

✕ ✕ ✕ ✕ ✕ ✕ ✕ ✕ ✕ ✕ ✕

DEAR GOD

TODAY I THANK YOU FOR:

1. _____

2. _____

3. _____

TODAY I ASK YOU FOR: _____

_____

TODAY I AM PRAYING FOR THESE PEOPLE:

1. _____

2. _____

3. _____

TODAY'S BIBLE VERSE/STORY: _____

_____

_____

now I lay me down to sleep....

TONIGHT I PRAY FOR: _____

TONIGHT I THANK GOD FOR: _____

TONIGHT _____
    IS ON MY HEART

amen.

TODAY'S DATE: _____ S M T W Th F S

✗ ✗ ✗ ✗ ✗ ✗ ✗ ✗ ✗ ✗ ✗

DEAR GOD

TODAY I THANK YOU FOR:

1. _____

2. _____

3. _____

TODAY I ASK YOU FOR: _____

_____

TODAY I AM PRAYING FOR THESE PEOPLE:

1. _____

2. _____

3. _____

TODAY'S BIBLE VERSE/STORY: _____

_____

_____

now I lay me down to sleep....

TONIGHT I PRAY FOR: _____

TONIGHT I THANK GOD FOR: _____

TONIGHT _____
    IS ON MY HEART

amen.

TODAY'S DATE: _____ S M T W Th F S

✕ ✕ ✕ ✕ ✕ ✕ ✕ ✕ ✕ ✕ ✕ **DEAR GOD**

TODAY I THANK YOU FOR:

1. _____
2. _____
3. _____

TODAY I ASK YOU FOR: _____
_____

TODAY I AM PRAYING FOR THESE PEOPLE:

1. _____
2. _____
3. _____

TODAY'S BIBLE VERSE/STORY: _____
_____
_____

now I lay me down to sleep....

TONIGHT I PRAY FOR: _____

TONIGHT I THANK GOD FOR: _____

TONIGHT _____
  IS ON MY HEART

amen.

TODAY'S DATE: _____ S M T W Th F S

✕ ✕ ✕ ✕ ✕ ✕ ✕ ✕ ✕ ✕ ✕

DEAR GOD

TODAY I THANK YOU FOR:

1. _____

2. _____

3. _____

TODAY I ASK YOU FOR: _____

_____

TODAY I AM PRAYING FOR THESE PEOPLE:

1. _____

2. _____

3. _____

TODAY'S BIBLE VERSE/STORY: _____

_____

_____

now I lay me down to sleep....

TONIGHT I PRAY FOR: _____

TONIGHT I THANK GOD FOR: _____

TONIGHT _____
    IS ON MY HEART

amen.

TODAY'S DATE: _____ S M T W Th F S

✗ ✗ ✗ ✗ ✗ ✗ ✗ ✗ ✗ ✗ ✗

DEAR GOD

TODAY I THANK YOU FOR:

1. _____
2. _____
3. _____

TODAY I ASK YOU FOR: _____

_____

TODAY I AM PRAYING FOR THESE PEOPLE:

1. _____
2. _____
3. _____

TODAY'S BIBLE VERSE/STORY: _____

_____

_____

now I lay me down to sleep....

TONIGHT I PRAY FOR: _____

TONIGHT I THANK GOD FOR: _____

TONIGHT _____
  IS ON MY HEART

amen.